Better Vocals 1

Rockschool

A *Rockschool* Publication
www.rockschool.co.uk

Welcome To Level 2 *Female Vocals*

Welcome to the Rockschool Level 2 candidate pack for Female Vocals. This pack includes all the prepared elements needed by a candidate to take grades 4 and 5. In the book you will find exam scores for the performance pieces consisting of a vocal line and chord boxes.

The CDs have backing tracks for the technical exercises and backing tracks for each song. Examples of all the other tests contained in the exam can be found in the *Companion Guide* accompanying this series.

If you have any queries about this or any other Rockschool exam, please call us on **020 8332 6303** or email us at office@rockschool.co.uk. Visit our website http://www.rockschool.co.uk. Good luck!

Grade 4

Pieces at this grade will be of sufficient length to demonstrate developing stylistic awareness which will include appropriate tone production, awareness of rhythmic shifts, dynamics and phrasing. There will be demonstration of secure chest voice and the ability to move to head voice in a reliable manner. Pieces will require some ornamentation and improvisation to the given line to show a musical understanding. Range will be extended and there will be some use of consistent extended intervals. **One piece is to be performed from memory. Performers must use a microphone for all performance pieces.**

Grade 5

At this level the candidate will be expected to demonstrate a good understanding of stylistic matters. Pieces will be of a suitable length to reflect this and will be shown by tonal variety, stylistic rhythmic execution a broader understanding and control of dynamics and phrasing. The candidate will demonstrate both chest and head voice in a secure manner with the ability to cover wide intervals with an even tone. Pieces will have the opportunity for considerable ornamentation and improvisation. **Two pieces are to be performed from memory. Performers must use a microphone for all performance pieces.**

How To Use The CD

The Level 2 book contains a CD. On these you will find the backing tracks to the exercises and the songs. You should prepare the exercises and the songs using this CD to perform with in the exam.

For the scales and intervals in grades 4 and 5, the first backing track is in the key of A. You will find alternative keys for the scales at the end of the CD in all keys between B♭ and D around middle C. For the intervals, test 1, there are alternative notes from B♭ to A, and for test 2, there are alternative notes from F to E. Any of these keys can be used in the exam.

Important Information For Candidates

Candidates may use this syllabus to enter for either a **grade exam** or a **performance certificate** at grades 4 or 5. If you are entering for a **grade exam**, you will need to prepare the following elements. You will perform them in the exam in the order in which they are shown below. Full syllabus requirements can be found in the *Rockschool Vocal Syllabus Guide* which can be downloaded from www.rockschool.co.uk.

Technical exercises (15 marks). You will find four sets of exercises printed for each grade: a rhythm test, a scale test, an interval test and a Phrasing & Dynamics test.

General Musicianship Questions (5 marks). You will be asked four questions immediately after the Phrasing & Dynamics test. These questions will focus on aspects of music notation. One final question will be asked at the end of the exam. Please refer to the *Syllabus Guide* for the GMQ requirements.

Aural Tests (10 marks). There are two aural tests in each grade. Examples are printed in the *Companion Guide*. The requirements for each grade are as follows:

• **Grade 4**. You will be given a sheet with three rhythmic examples that are two bars long each. The examiner will play one of the examples on CD and you will be asked to identify the correct answer from the printed examples and clap back the rhythm. You will then be given three melodic examples in the same rhythms as above of two bars each. You will be asked to identify the test with the correct rhythm. You will then be asked to sight sing the examples and continue for two bars, ending on the tonic or the mediant. The second test will be a four bar chord sequence repeated over 8 bars. You will hear the sequence once and will be required to improvise a minor pentatonic line, paying attention to the rhythmic idea and shape on the repeat. **This test is continuous.**

• **Grade 5**. Test 1: as for Grade 4. The second test will be a four bar chord sequence repeated over 8 bars. You will hear the sequence once and will be required to improvise a minor pentatonic or blues line, paying attention to the style, rhythmic idea and shape on the repeat. **This test is continuous**.

Three performance pieces (60 marks). You are not limited solely to the songs printed in this book, or the companion Level 1 volume. You may perform **either** three songs from this book (including one or more from the supplementary list printed for each grade), **or** you may bring in **one** song not included in these lists to perform in the exam. This may be a hit from the chart or a song of your own composing. Please ensure, though, that you have the appropriate backing track. Please turn to the Guru's Guide on page 45 for the list of supplementary material.

Unaccompanied Piece (10 Marks). In addition, you will be asked to perform either a part of one of the pieces you have performed, or a different song, unaccompanied. You will be asked to sing this after you have performed the second accompanied song you have chosen. Please refer to the *Syllabus Guide* for the variation and improvisation requirements.

If you are entering a **performance certificate**, you will perform **five** songs, of which up to **two** may be from repertoire not included in this book or the companion Level 1 volume.

The Level 2 *Female Vocals* book is a companion to the Level 2 *Male Vocals* book. Candidates are welcome to perform repertoire contained in either book in the exam of equivalent difficulty.

Grade 4 *Technical Exercises*

In this section, the examiner will ask you to perform the four exercises printed below. You do not need to memorise the exercises (and you may use the book in the exam) but the examiner will be looking for the speed and confidence of your response. The examiner will also give you credit for the level of your musicality in your attention to directions, including phrasing and dynamics.

Exercise 1: Rhythm

Track 1

You will be asked to perform the exercise below as written to a backing track accompaniment in the exam. A short sound check will be given.

You will be asked to perform a major, natural minor, major pentatonic and minor pentatonic scale with arpeggios in the following rhythms to a backing track accompaniment in the exam. You will be allowed to choose your own starting note between **A-D** which will be played to you before you begin. You will be asked a selection by the examiner and you will perform the exercise *legato* to a sound of your own choosing.

Major

Natural Minor

Major Pentatonic

Minor Pentatonic

Exercise 3: Intervals

This exercise has two parts. (A) You will be asked to pitch a major or minor third, perfect fourth and perfect fifth by step and back to the third above notes **I, IV** and **V** of the chosen key of the above scale. The examiner will play the note for four beats on a CD and you will be asked to sing as indicated.

(B) You will be asked to pitch the root to major or minor third by step and back to tonic below the perfect fifth of the tonic notes of the above test. The examiner will play the interval for four beats on a CD and you will be asked to sing as indicated.

Exercise 4: Phrasing & Dynamics

You will be asked to prepare the following exercise. The examiner will play the backing on CD and you will be asked to sing the exercise, paying attention to the written phrasing and dynamics. You may perform the exercise using any sound that you consider appropriate.

Son Of A Preacher Man

Words & Music by
John Hurley & Ronnie Wilkins

Verse 2 :

Being good isn't always easy
No matter how hard I try .
When he started sweet talking to me,
He'd come and tell me everything is all right,
He'd kiss and tell me everything is all right ,
Can't get away again tonight .

I'm Not A Girl, Not Yet A Woman

Words & Music by
Max Martin, Rami & Dido

Track 7

Vocals Level 2 - Female

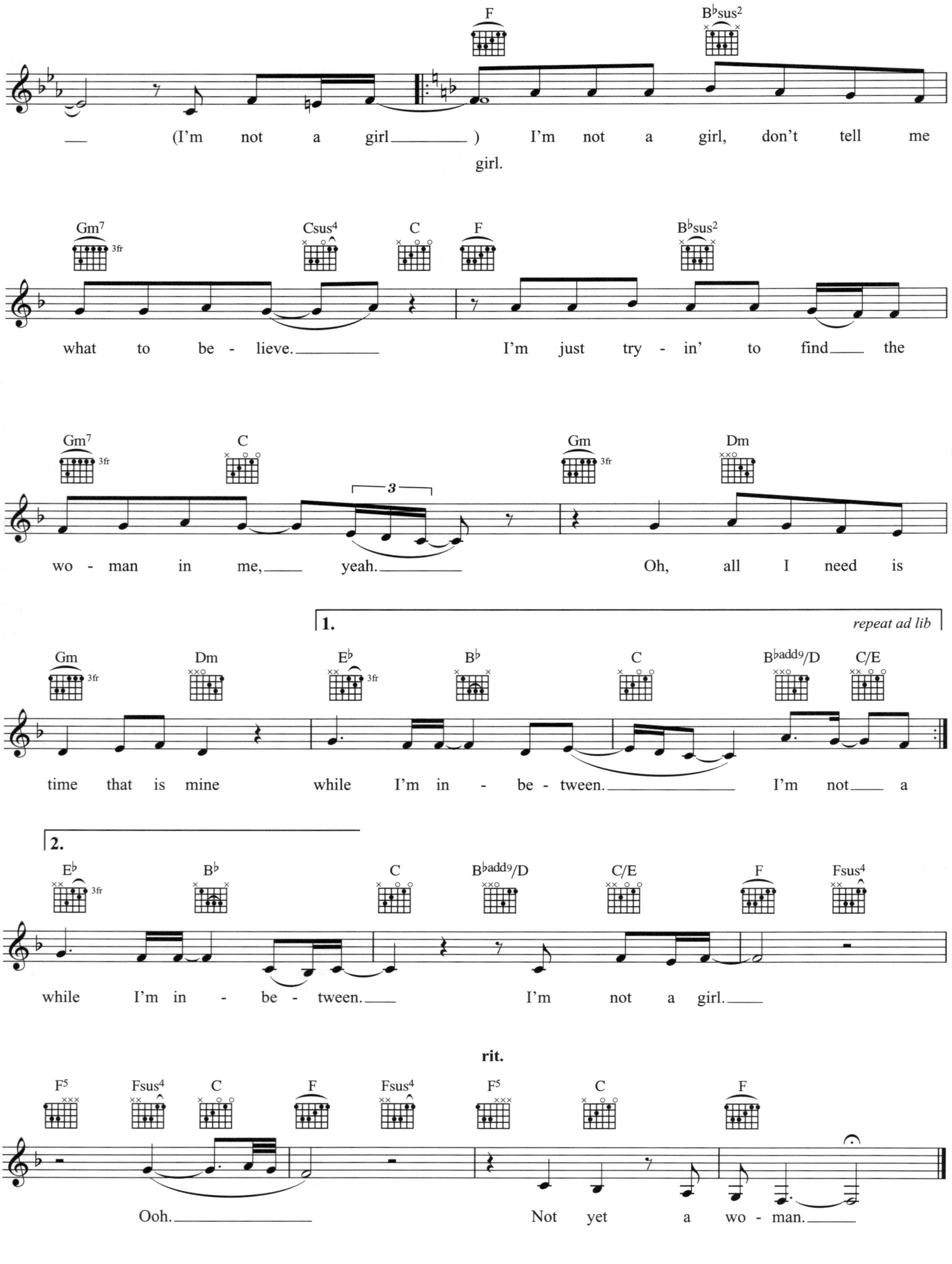
F
B♭sus2
(I'm not a girl) I'm not a girl, don't tell me
girl.
Gm7
3fr
Csus4
C
F
B♭sus2
what to be - lieve.
I'm just try - in' to find the
Gm7
3fr
C
3
Gm
3fr
Dm
wo - man in me, yeah.
Oh, all I need is
1.
repeat ad lib
Gm
3fr
Dm
E♭
3fr
B♭
C
B♭add9/D
C/E
time that is mine
while I'm in - be - tween.
I'm not a
2.
E♭
3fr
B♭
C
B♭add9/D
C/E
F
Fsus4
while I'm in - be - tween.
I'm not a girl.
rit.
F5
Fsus4
C
F
Fsus4
F5
C
F
Ooh.
Not yet a wo - man.

A Thousand Miles

Words & Music by Vanessa Carlton

Track 8

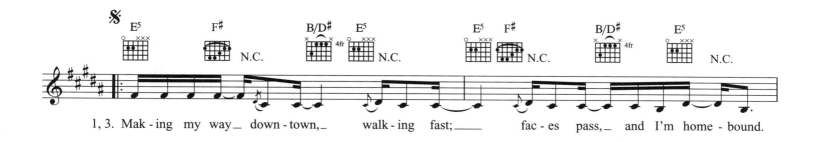

1, 3. Mak - ing my way_ down - town,_ walk - ing fast;____ fac - es pass,_ and I'm home - bound.

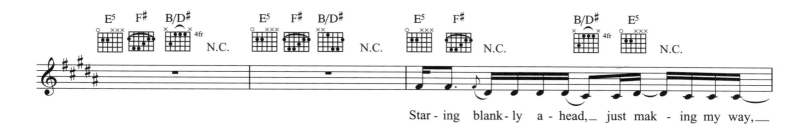

Star - ing blank - ly a - head,_ just mak - ing my way,__

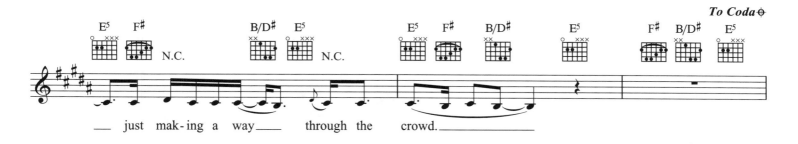

___ just mak - ing a way__ through the crowd.____

To Coda

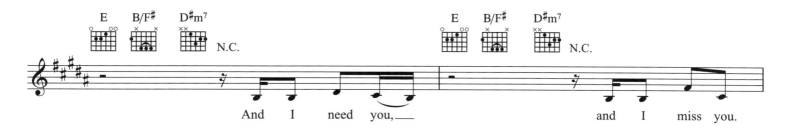

And I need you,__ and I miss you.

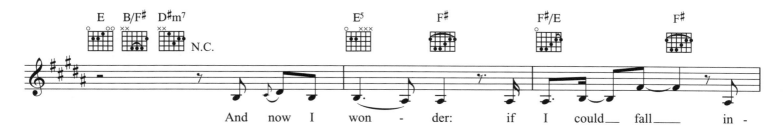

And now I won - der: if I could__ fall__ in -

Verse 2:

It's always times like these
When I think of you
And I wonder if you ever think of me.
'Cause everything's so wrong
And I don't belong
Living in your precious memory.
'Cause I need you
And I miss you
And now I wonder:

If I could fall into the sky *etc.*

Don't Speak

Words & Music by
Eric Stefani & Gwen Stefani

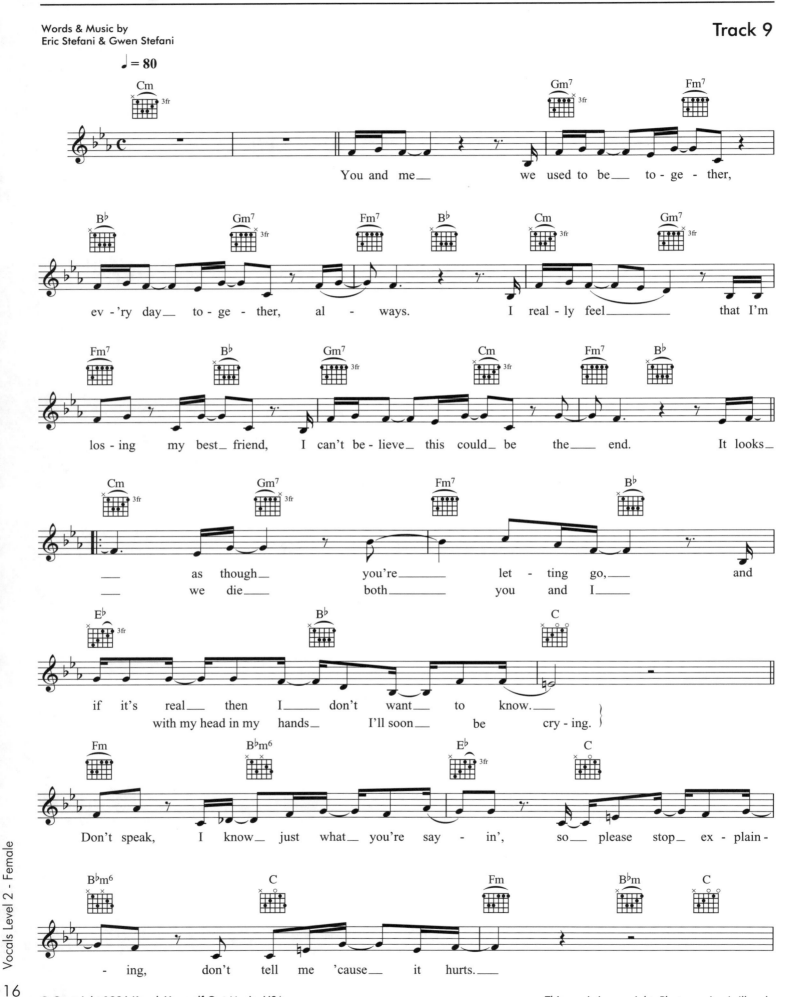

16

Vocals Level 2 - Female

Don't speak, I___ know what___ you're think - in', I don't need___ your rea- - sons, don't tell me 'cause___ it hurts.___ Old me - mo - ries,___ they can be___ in - vit - ing, but some are all to - ge - ther migh - ty fright - 'ning. As___

It's all end - ing,___ we've got to stop pre - tend - ing who we are.

Whenever, Wherever

Words by Shakira & Gloria Estefan
Music by Shakira & Tim Mitchell

Track 10

(Ah.) _____ (Ah.) _____ (Oh.) _____

(Oh.) _____ (Oh.) _____

1. Luck-y you were born that far a-way so_____ we could both make fun of dis-tance.

(Verse 2 see block lyric)

Luck-y that I love a for-eign land for_____ the luck-y fact of your ex-ist-ence.

Ba-by I would climb the An-des sole-ly_____ to count the freck-les on your bo-dy.

Nev-er could i-ma-gine there were on-ly ten mil-lion ways to love some-bo-dy.

Le do le le le le._____ Le do le le le le._____

Vocals Level 2 - Female

Verse 2:

Lucky that my lips not only mumble
They spill kisses like a fountain
Lucky that my breasts are small and humble
So you don't confuse them with mountains.
Lucky I have strong legs like my mother
To run for cover when I need it
And these two eyes are for no other
The day you leave will cry a river.
Le do le le le le, le do le le le le
At your feet, I'm at your feet.

Whenever, wherever *etc.*

Torn

Words & Music by Anne Preven,
Scott Cutler & Phil Thornalley

♩ = 97

1. I thought I saw___ a man___ brought___ to life._____ He was warm,___

___ he came a-round___ like he was dig - ni - fied.___ He showed me what it was___ to cry.___

Well, you could-n't be___ that man___ I a - dored.___
(Verse 2 see block lyric)

You don't seem to know,___ don't seem to care___ what your

heart is for.___ But I don't know___ him a-ny-more.___ There's

no-thing where___ he used to lie,___ con-ver-sa-tion has run dry.___
(Verse 3 see block lyric)

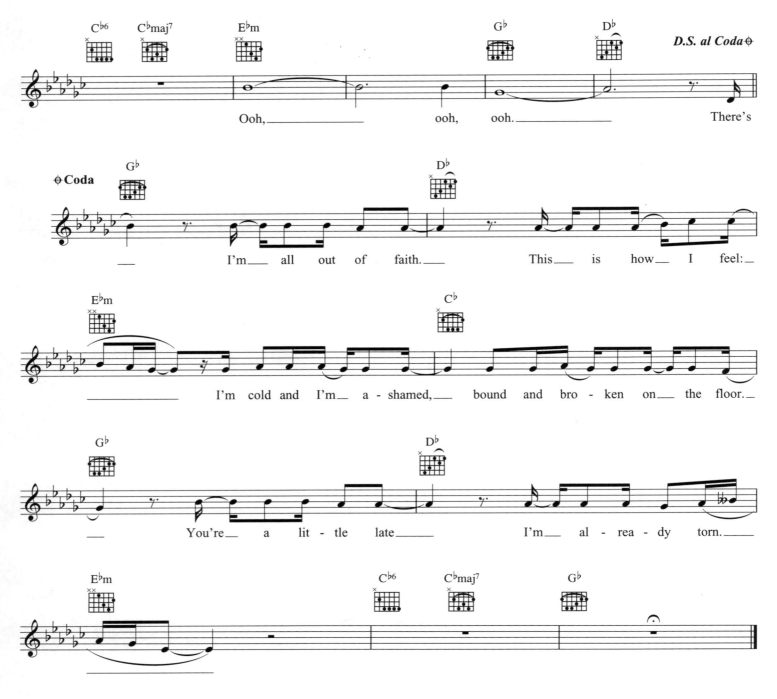

Verse 2:

So I guess the fortune-teller's right.
I should have seen just what was there, and not some holy light.
But you crawled beneath my veins
And now I don't care I had no luck.
I don't miss it all that much.
There's just so many things that I can search.

I'm torn *etc.*

Verse 3:

There's nothing where he used to lie.
My inspiration has run dry.
That's what's going on:
Nothing's right.

I'm torn *etc.*

Entering An Exam

Please use one, or a combination, of these forms to enter the exam(s) of your choice. Fill out the details as requested below and send the form, along with the appropriate fees, to:

Exam Entries, Rock School Ltd, 245 Sandycombe Road, Kew, Surrey, TW9 2EW

There are three examination periods per year for which you may enter. The closing dates for these are shown in the table below.

PERIOD	DURATION	CLOSING DATE
Period A	1st February to 15th March	1st December
Period B	15th May to 31st July	1st April
Period C	1st November to 15th December	1st October

You can get up-to-date information on examination prices by ringing the Rockschool help line on **020 8332 6303** Please make cheques or postal orders payable to **Rock School Ltd**.

Exam Entry Form

Full Name	
Address	
Post Code	
Telephone	
Please tick one	Grade ☐ Performance Certificates ☐
Grade	1 ☐ 2 ☐ 3 ☐ 4 ☐ 5 ☐ 6 ☐ 7 ☐ 8 ☐
Period	A ☐ B ☐ C ☐
Year	
Fee	
Dates that are absolutely impossible for you to attend:	

Teacher's Exam Entry Form

Teachers wishing to enter grade exams and performance certificates on behalf of their students should complete the form and send it, along with the appropriate fees, to

Exam Entries, Rock School Ltd, 245 Sandycombe Road, Kew, Surrey, TW9 2EW

You can get up to date information on examination prices by ringing the Rockschool help line on **020 8332 6303** Please make cheques or postal orders payable to **Rock School Ltd**.

Teacher's Name	
Address	
	Post Code
Telephone	

Name	Grade	Perf.Cert	Period	Year	Fee
				Total fees enclosed	£

Dates that are absolutely impossible for you to attend:

Vocal Exam Regulations

1. Rockschool exams are open to all persons, irrespective of age.

2. Full payment and relevant documentation must reach the offices of Rockschool on or before the chosen exam period's closing date. Rockschool cannot guarantee an exam for any applications received after this date.

3. Candidates may not transfer an exam from one exam centre to another.

4. Exam entries may not be transferred from one candidate to another.

5. Cancellation of an exam will result in loss of the exam fee unless as a result of illness or injury. Such cases must be substantiated by a medical certificate. In this event, the exam will be re-scheduled on receipt of half of the original exam fee.

6. On application, candidates may state times within an exam period when they are unavailable. However, Rockschool cannot guarantee to avoid all such dates.

7. Rockschool reserves the right to defer exams until the next available exam period. After one deferral, an exam is guaranteed at an exam centre chosen by Rockschool. This may not be your local centre.

8. Candidates must use only the official Rockschool sheet music for their respective exam. Photocopying of any material contained within the official published pack is prohibited. You may not use a Rockschool pack already used by someone else in another exam. This will result in disqualification.

9. No refunds are given.

10. No teacher, or other person, must be present during the preparation of a candidate's Quick Study Piece. Any assistance given to a candidate will result in disqualification from the examination.

11. Only the examiner and candidate are allowed to be present in the examination room with the exception of external moderators or trainee examiners.

12. Candidates must bring in two copies of music for the 'free choice piece'. Players must use an original copy of the tune to be performed, and must provide a second copy for the examiner, which may be a photocopy. If there is no music available, a zero mark will be given for the piece. Any queries in writing should be addressed to the General Manager at least two weeks prior to the exam date.

13. Any special needs candidates must notify the Rockschool office prior to the exam.

14. The examiner's decision is final. Normally, an examiner will hear every component in full, but on occasion an examiner may conclude an examination when a decision has been reached.

15. Rockschool operates a quality assured appeals process, moderated by Trinity College London. All appeals must be made in writing no later than 14 days after the exam date. There are two criteria for formal appeals, these are:
    - Appeals in respect of errors in procedure.
    - Appeals in respect of errors in matching comments to marks awarded.

16. Candidates may use microphones for the lower grades (grades 1-5) but must inform the office of their intention to do so.

Grade 5 *Technical Exercises*

In this section, the examiner will ask you to perform the four exercises printed below. You do not need to memorise the exercises (and you may use the book in the exam) but the examiner will be looking for the speed and confidence of your response. The examiner will also give you credit for the level of your musicality in your attention to directions, including phrasing and dynamics.

Exercise 1: Rhythm   Track 12

You will be asked to perform the exercise below as written to a backing track accompaniment in the exam. A short sound check will be given.

Exercise 2: Scales

You will be asked to perform a major and natural minor with arpeggios and a minor pentatonic and blues scale in the following rhythms to a backing track accompaniment in the exam. You will be allowed to choose your own starting note between **A-D** which will be played to you before you begin. You will be asked a selection by the examiner and you will perform the exercise *legato* or *staccato* to a sound of your own choosing.

Major Scale and Arpeggio   Track 13

to be prepared *legato* and *staccato*

Natural Minor Scale and Arpeggio   Track 14

Minor Pentatonic Scale   Track 15

Blues Scale   Track 15

Exercise 3: Intervals

You should prepare all three parts of a chordal sequence using chords **I**, **IV** and **V**. The examiner will select the part to be given against the other two parts played on a backing track.

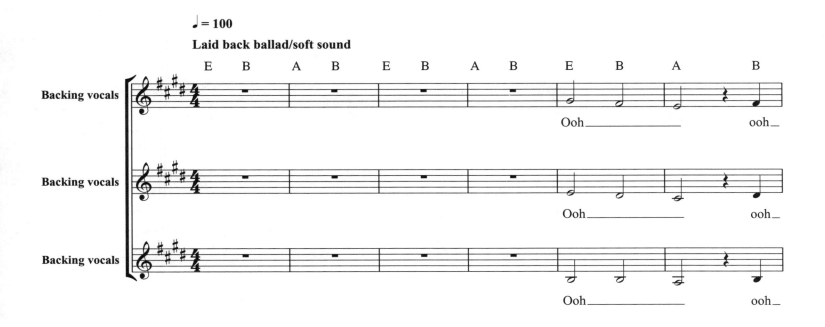

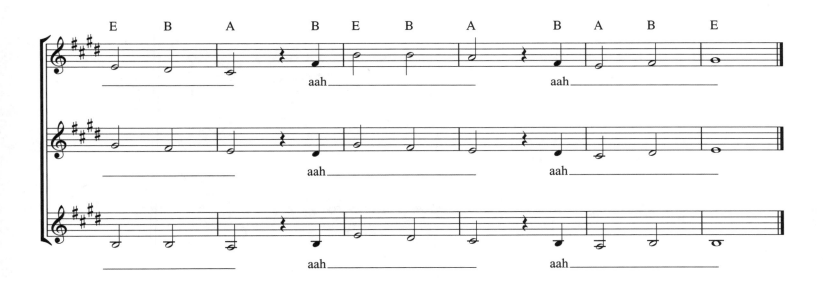

Vocals Level 2 - Female

Exercise 4: Phrasing & Dynamics

You will be asked to prepare the following exercise. The examiner will play the backing on CD and you will be asked to sing the exercise, paying attention to the written phrasing and dynamics. You may perform the exercise using any sound that you consider appropriate.

I Turn To You

Words & Music by Melanie Chisholm,
Rick Nowels & Billy Steinberg

♩ = 136

Lyrics:

1. When the world is dark - er than I can un - der - stand, when no - thing turns out the way I planned, and there's no end in sight.

2. When my in - sides are wracked with an - xi - e - ty, You have the touch that will qui - et me. - rit, you melt the ice.

when the sky turns grey when I can't sleep through the lone - ly night, I turn to you,

You lift my spi - When I need in - spi - ra - tion, when I need ad - vice,

Ah. Ah.

to___ you.___

I

turn to you like a flow-er lean - ing to - ward___ the sun.___
(2°) when fear tells___ me to turn___ a - round.___

I turn to you___ 'cause you're the on - ly one___

who can turn___ me a - round___ when I'm up - side___ down___

1.

I turn to you.___ I turn to

2.

___ I turn to you.___

Ironic

Words by Alanis Morissette
Music by Alanis Morissette & Glen Ballard

32 © Copyright 1995 Music Corporation Of America Incorporated/
Vanhurst Place Music/MCA Music Publishing/Aerostation Corporation, USA.
Universal/MCA Music Limited.
All Rights Reserved. International Copyright Secured.

This music is copyright. Photocopying is illegal.

Verse 2:

Mister Play It Safe was afraid to fly
He packed his suitcase and kissed his kids goodbye
He waited his whole damn life to take that flight
And as the plane crashed down he thought, "Well isn't this nice?"

It's like rain *etc.*

Kiss Kiss

Words & Music by Aksu Sezen,
Juliette Jaimes & Steve Welton-Jaimes

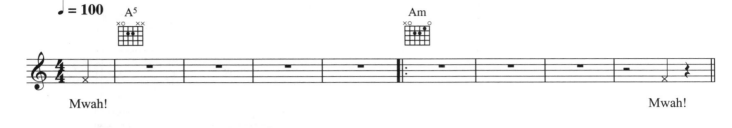

Mwah!   Mwah!

1. When you look at me, tell me what you see. This is what you get, it's the way I am.

(Verse 2 see block lyric)

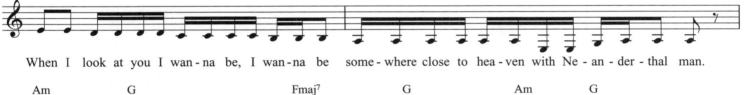

When I look at you I wan‑na be, I wan‑na be some‑where close to hea‑ven with Ne‑an‑der‑thal man.

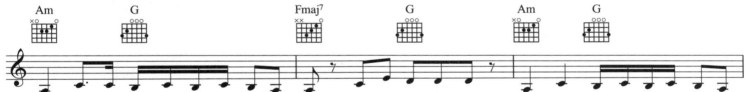

Don't go, I know you wan‑na touch me, here, there and ev‑'ry‑where. Sparks fly when we are to‑geth‑er,

you can't de‑ny the facts of life._____ You don't have to act like a star,_____ try‑ing

moves in the back of your car._____ But you know that we can go far,_____ 'cause to‑

‑night you're gon‑na get my._ (Kiss kiss.) Don't play the games that you play,_____ 'cause you

Vocals Level 2 - Female

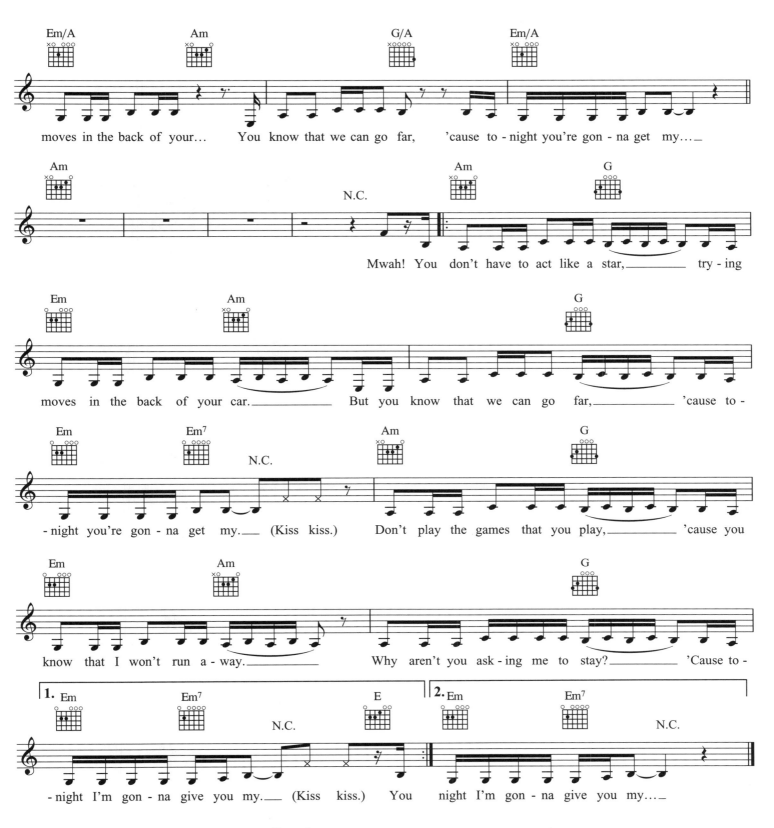

Verse 2:

You could be mine baby, what's your star sign?
Won't you take a step into the lions' den?
I can hear my conscience calling me, calling me
Say'n I'm gonna be a bad girl again.
Why don't you come on over, we can't leave this all undone
Got a devil on my shoulder, there's no place for you to run.

You don't have to act *etc.*

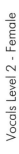

Save The Best For Last

Words & Music by Jon Lind,
Wendy Waldman & Philip Galdston

Track 23

38

I Say A Little Prayer

Words by Hal David
Music by Burt Bacharach

Track 24

Verse

1. The mo-ment I wake up, be-fore I put
2. I run for the bus dear, while ri-ding I

on my make-up, I say a lit-tle prayer for you.
think of us dear, I say a lit-tle prayer for you.

While comb-ing my hair now, and won-d'ring what dress to
At work I just take time, and through my cof-fee

wear now, I say a lit-tle prayer for you. For-
break time, I say a lit-tle prayer for you.

Chorus

-ev-er, for-ev-er you'll stay in my heart and I will love you, for-

Vocals Level 2 - Female

40

© Copyright 1966 Blue Seas Music Incorporated/Casa David Music Incorporated, USA.
Windswept Music (London) Limited (50%)/Universal/MCA Music Limited (50%).
All Rights Reserved. International Copyright Secured.

This music is copyright. Photocopying is illegal.

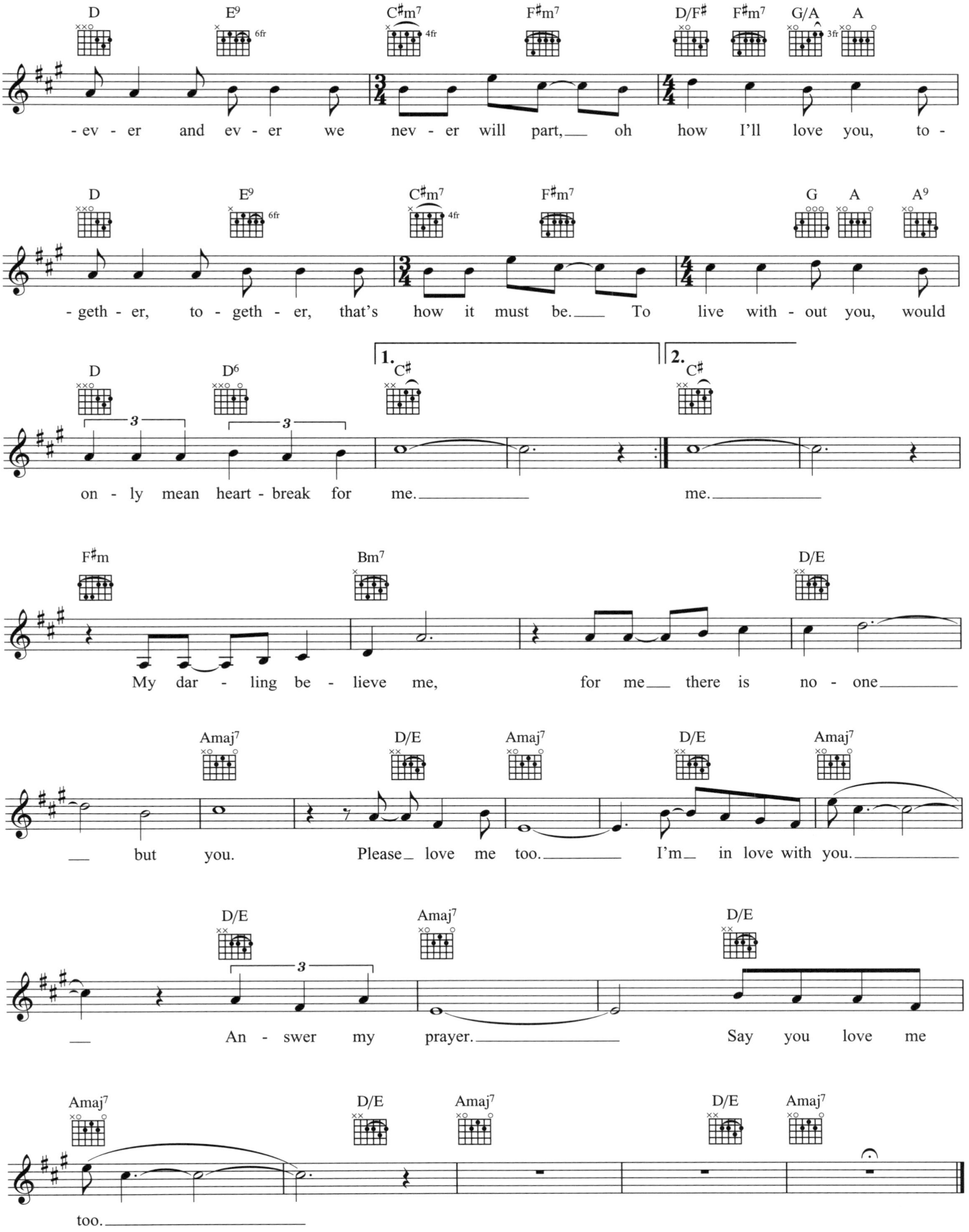

My Love Is Your Love

Words & Music by
Wyclef Jean & Jerry Duplessis

Track 25

Vocals Level 2 - Female

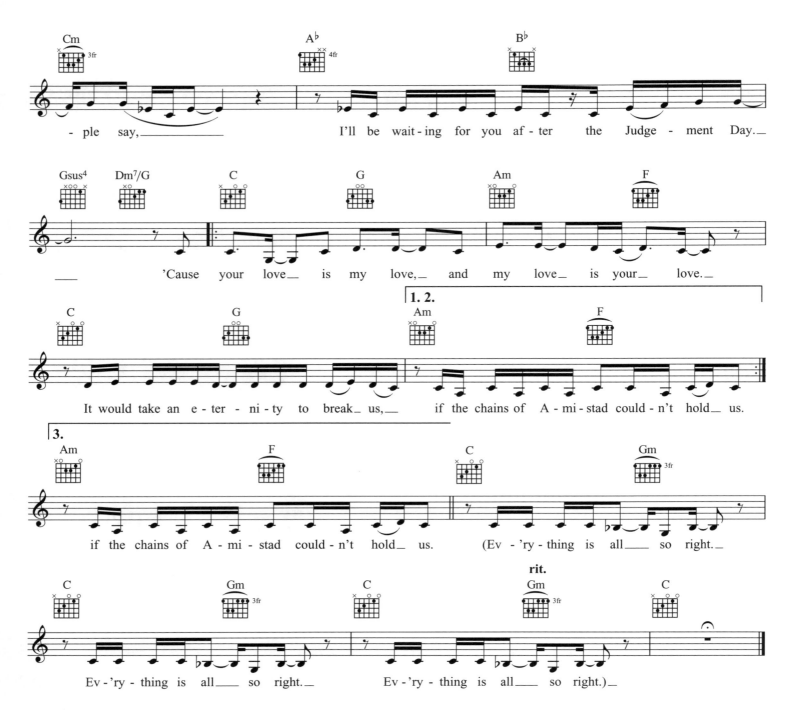

The Guru's Guide To Level 2 *Female Vocals*

Supplementary Material

Rockschool recommends the following songs in addition to the repertoire printed in this book. The list below shows the songs arranged by grade along with the publications in which they may be found.

Grade 4

Hungry	*Sing 16 Hits*	AM976800
Walk On By	*Essential Audition Songs: Pop Ballads*	IMP6939A
I Will Survive	*Audition Songs For Female Singers 1*	AM92587
Promise Me	*Essential Audition Songs: Pop Ballads*	IMP6939A
The First Time Ever I Saw Your Face	*Sing & Party With Tear-jerkers*	IMP9803A
Perfect Moment	*Audition Songs For Professional Singers*	AM974578
Breathless	*Audition Songs For Professional Singers*	AM974578
Black Velvet	*Audition Songs For Professional Singers*	AM974578
Road Rage	*Audition Songs For Female Singers*	AM966658
From A Distance	*Audition Songs For Professional Singers*	AM974578
That Ole Devil Called Love	*Audition Songs For Female Singers 3*	AM955284
You Gotta Be	*Audition Songs For Female Singers 6*	AM963776
Superwoman	*All Woman 1*	IMP7077A

Grade 5

Without You	*Essential Audition Songs: Pop Divas*	IMP7769A
Natural Woman	*The Voice: Carol King*	IMP9700A
Family Affair	*Audition Songs For Professional Singers*	AM974578
You Don't Have To Say You Love Me	*All Woman 2*	IMP7628A
Piece Of My Heart	*Audition songs For Female Singers 9*	AM966670
Believe	*Essential Audition Songs: Pop Divas*	IMP7769A
American Pie	*Audition Songs For Professional Singers*	AM974578

Warm Up

It is important that you prepare for the exam by warming up your voice properly. You should ensure that you arrive at the exam centre within plenty of time to do this. We have arranged the elements of the grade exam such that the performances come at the end. The backing tracks and/or accompaniment are always variable in volume and you should always tell the examiner if you feel that you are straining to be heard.

Free Choice Pieces

In grade exams you are allowed to perform one song not specified in this book or the companion Level 2 *Male Vocals* book. This may be a hit from the chart or a song composed by yourself. In performance certificate exams you are allowed to perform up to two songs not specified in this book.

If you wish to find out whether a free choice piece song is appropriate for the grade, you may either contact Rockschool and submit the song for adjudication, or look on our website www.rockschool.co.uk and consult the free choice piece criteria.

Marking Schemes

The table below shows the marking schemes for grad exams and performance certificates. All Rockschool exams are marked out of 100 and the pass mark for a grade exam is 65% and for a performance certificate is 70%.

Grade Exam

Element	Pass	Merit	Distinction
Technical Exercises	11 out of 15	12 out of 15	13 out of 15
General Musicianship Questions	3 out of 5	4 out of 5	5 out of 5
Aural Tests	6 out of 10	7 out of 10	8 out of 10
Piece 1	13 out of 20	15 out of 20	17 out of 20
Piece 2	13 out of 20	15 out of 20	17 out of 20
Piece 3	13 out of 20	15 out of 20	17 out of 20
Unaccompanied Piece	6 out of 10	7 out of 10	7 out of 10

Performance Certificate

Element	Pass	Merit	Distinction
Piece 1	14 out of 20	16 out of 20	18 out of 20
Piece 2	14 out of 20	16 out of 20	18 out of 20
Piece 3	14 out of 20	16 out of 20	18 out of 20
Piece 4	14 out of 20	16 out of 20	18 out of 20
Piece 5	14 out of 20	16 out of 20	18 out of 20

Examination Criteria

Rockschool examiners assess all examinations according to strict guidelines. Copies of these for vocals can be found on the website www.rockschool.co.uk or direct from our offices. Please ring **020 8332 6303** for further details.

Exam Regulations

Entering a Rockschool exam is easy. Please read through the instructions on the back of the entry form accompanying this book carefully, before filling it in. Information on current fees can be obtained by ringing Rockschool on **020 8332 6303** or by logging on to the website www.rockschool.co.uk.